It's another Quality Book from CGP

This book has been carefully written for Key Stage Two children preparing for the reading part of the Year 6 SATs. It's full of tricky questions covering all seven of the reading Assessment Focuses:

- AF1 Understand the **meaning** of a text ← *AF1 isn't specifically tested in the SAT, but it underpins all the other Assessment Focuses.*
- AF2 Select and **retrieve** information
- AF3 **Infer** information and ideas
- AF4 Understand **structural** and **layout** features
- AF5 Understand **language** features
- AF6 Interpret the **writer's purpose**
- AF7 Relate texts to their **context**

In this book we've separated the questions out so children can learn how to spot questions on each Assessment Focus and give exactly the right kind of answer.

Children can use the Reading Raptor tick boxes for self-assessment, which helps you work out how they're getting on with each Assessment Focus.

Published by CGP

Written by:
Chris Fenton

Editors:
Joe Brazier, Camilla Simson, Rachel Ward

Many thanks to Samantha Bensted and David Broadbent for proofreading.

ISBN: 978 1 84146 165 6

Groovy website: www.cgpbooks.co.uk
Jolly bits of clipart from CorelDRAW®
Printed by Elanders Ltd, Newcastle upon Tyne.

Based on the classic CGP style created by Richard Parsons.

Inference Questions

For INFERENCE questions you need to work out what's happened or how a character feels, even if the text doesn't spell it out. See you if you can work out the answers to these.

1. What is **'the darkness'**?

 .... **1 mark**

2. What are the **'loud whizzing stones'**?

 .... **1 mark**

3. The animal could not find his **'brothers'** because

they were hiding from him	**they were lost**	**they had been killed by humans**	**they were camouflaged**

 1 mark

 Put a ring around your choice.

4. What do you think the creature is doing when the author uses the words **'chased and pounced'**?

 .... **1 mark**

5. **'Walking on the dusty bones and dirt of my ancestors**
 As my children would walk on mine.'

 From this sentence, do you think the animal is scared of dying? Explain your answer. **2 marks**

 ....

 ....

 ....

6. How do you think the creature feels when he realises he is not dead?

 .... **1 mark**

Saved?

I am a proud, proud beast from the Serengeti.
I prowled my land with puffed-up chest,
Walking on the dusty bones and dirt of my ancestors
As my children would walk on mine.
Every day the wind brought with it the smell of my land.
The distant scent of fear my presence presented
Fuelled my strides as I chased and pounced.
The darkness was swift for my victims.
There was no anger from them for they knew a sacred cycle of life had been completed –
And that they would be greeted in the darkness.

Then Man came.

My brothers became the victims, felled by loud whizzing stones that broke their flesh and took their life.
I searched for the roars of my brothers but was deceived by the rushing waterfalls.
I sought the scent of my brothers but was tricked by the smells of the wild.
I hunted for the sight of my brothers but was fooled by the stripes in the sunlit reeds.
What unnatural cycle was this?

Then Man came.

Now swift poison darts broke my skin and closed my eyes.
I awoke not in the darkness with my victims but in a silent man-cage of steel.
I hoped to be greeted by ancestors –
But was not.
Cold grey dust pushed against my feet as I awoke and the stripes I saw were metal.
The wind was heavy with foreign smells and the men and their cubs stared.

I am a proud, proud beast of the Serengeti
But now I am saved from it – how I wish I was still there.

C J Fenton

Saved? — Poem

Poems are fancy bits of writing, usually written in short lines, and with strong ideas or feelings in them. Sometimes they have a bit of a rhythm and sometimes they don't. They're often written by quiet people with long hair and glasses, and they can come up in the SAT.

What to do —

1) Open out the folding page and read the poem *Saved?*
2) When you've read it, see if you can stand on one leg for a minute, then read it again.
3) Once you've done that, you can go on to the questions.

Inference Questions

AF3

7. What type of smells do you think would make the air **'heavy'**?

....

1 mark

8. Find and copy a phrase from the poem that describes the fact that all animals will eventually die or be killed, and that this provides food for other animals.

....

1 mark

9. Who is the creature talking about when it says **'cubs'**?

....

1 mark

10. Why do you think the creature was **'deceived'** by the sound of the waterfall?

....

....

1 mark

11. Tick two boxes to show how the creature is feeling at the **beginning** and **end** of the poem.

Proud to be showing off in the cage ☐

Proud to be born free and living free ☐

Happy because he won't have to hunt for his food in the cage ☐

Angry and confused and lonely ☐

Eager to make new friends ☐

2 marks

A Reading Raptor would know exactly what was going on in this poem. Did you? Tick to show how you did.

Inference Questions

Some of the INFERENCE questions get a bit trickier here, but don't panic. Carefully read through the poem again and see if you can answer these.

1. Find and copy a phrase from the poem that tells us that everything is about to change.

.... **1 mark**

2. Using evidence from the poem, explain what type of animal you think is speaking.

.... **2 marks**

....

3. **'But now I am saved from it — how I wish I was still there.'**
   Explain what this sentence means.

.... **2 marks**

....

4. What do you think the creature means when it says it **'hoped to be greeted by ancestors'**?

.... **2 marks**

....

5. **'Now swift poison darts broke my skin and closed my eyes.'**
   What do you think happened to the creature?

The creature was shot and killed	**The creature was shot and badly injured**	**The creature was shot and blinded**	**The creature was shot with drugs that knocked it out**

1 mark

Put a ring around your choice.

Inference Questions

6. Find and underline the phrase the writer uses to describe a quick death in these lines:

The distant scent of fear my presence presented
Fuelled my strides as I chased and pounced.
The darkness was swift for my victims.

1 mark

7. Why does the creature ask **'What unnatural cycle was this?'**

Answer the question as fully as you can, referring to the text where possible.

3 marks

....

....

....

....

8. How do you think the creature feels about humans?
Use evidence from the text to help you with your answer.

2 marks

....

....

....

9. How are the **'victims'** in the first verse different from those in the second verse?
Use evidence from the text in your answer.

2 marks

....

....

....

....

Reading Raptors can do inference questions faster than you can say 'reading raptor'. How did you do?

Fact Retrieval Questions

For FACT RETRIEVAL questions all you need to do is look in the poem for the bit of information you are asked for and write it down. Scan through the poem and find the answers to these.

1. At the beginning of the poem, how does the creature describe himself?

.... **1 mark**

2. Why weren't the creature's victims angry?

.... **1 mark**

3. How does the creature describe his cage?

.... **1 mark**

4. Find two words from the poem that suggest the creature is looking for his friends.

.... **2 marks**

....

5. Find and copy a phrase which is used more than once in the poem.

.... **1 mark**

6. What are the two different types of stripes that are described in the poem?

.... **2 marks**

....

Reading Raptors can find facts hidden on an unknown planet in outer space. How about you?

Writer's Purpose Questions

For WRITER'S PURPOSE questions you have to try and work out what ideas the writer was trying to communicate, or how they wanted the reader to feel.

1. Why do you think the author described the wind as **'heavy with foreign smells'**?

2 marks

....

....

2. 'I am a proud, proud beast from the Serengeti'

Why do you think the poem starts and ends with the same phrase?

2 marks

....

....

3. a) How does the author make you feel in the third verse?

Sad	Happy	Relieved

1 mark

Put a ring around your choice.

b) Explain your answer to part **a)** with reference to the text.

2 marks

....

....

4. How do you think the author feels about capturing animals to put in a zoo? How can you tell?

3 marks

....

....

....

Reading Raptors have special powers for working out what writers are trying to achieve. How did you do?

Language Questions

LANGUAGE questions are about working out why the author chose to use certain words or say things in a certain way. Read through the text again and have a go at these questions.

1. Underline two adjectives in the lines below:

Now swift poison darts broke my skin and closed my eyes.
I awoke not in the darkness with my victims but in a silent man-cage of steel.

2 marks

2. Which words show how confused the creature is after '**Man came**'?

3 marks

3. Why do you think the author chose to use the word **'darkness'** to refer to death?

2 marks

4. Why do you think the author chose the verb **'prowled'** in the second line of the poem?

2 marks

5. How does the author use contrast to tell the story of the creature? Refer to the text in your answer.

3 marks

Language Questions

6. Why do you think the author uses the word **'stripes'** when writing about the cage?

2 marks

....

....

7. Why do you think the author writes about the **'Cold grey dust'** in the cage?

2 marks

....

....

8. Why do you think there is a question mark in the title?
Answer the question as fully as you can, referring to the text where possible.

3 marks

....

....

....

....

9. **'I searched for the roars of my brothers but was deceived by the rushing waterfalls.**
I sought the scent of my brothers but was tricked by the smells of the wild.
I hunted for the sight of my brothers but was fooled by the stripes in the sunlit reeds.'

How do these lines affect the pace of the poem?

2 marks

....

....

Reading Raptors really love language questions.
How did you find the questions on these pages?

Inference Questions

Sometimes you need to do a bit of detective work to figure out exactly what's going on in the text. See if you can work out the answers to these INFERENCE questions.

1. Why do you think the breakfast was **'simple'**?

.... 1 mark

2. **'Its life had been dignified but its death had not.'**
Explain what this sentence means and why it is important to the story.

.... 2 marks

....

3. **'To them we were death. The creatures in these metal beasts stole their brothers and sisters and did not care for the wild at all'**
What are the **'metal beasts'**?

.... 1 mark

4. Using the information in the text, describe how the person who wrote the diary is feeling just before the team set off. Refer to the text in your answer.

.... 2 marks

....

5. **'It was a magnificent sight. Not that their strides were fuelled by fear but that they were free in the land of their birth.'**
How do you think the diarist was feeling at this point?
Answer the question as fully as you can.

.... 2 marks

....

Walking With Hunters

In her diary, wildlife photographer Anne le Trimel describes how she helped conservationists move a black rhinoceros from Namibia to a wildlife reserve in Kenya.

MONDAY 16 JUNE 2008

In the early hours of morning I arrived at base camp, where I met Bill Tresby, the expedition leader. As day broke, I was struck by the sense of calm in the new-born light.

Over a simple breakfast, Bill told me that animals in Africa were in danger, especially the black rhino. Rhino horn fetches a high price in many countries abroad, where it's used in traditional pills and potions. The punishments are harsh for poachers who get caught, but some are still lured by the promise of instant cash and risk their lives to kill a black rhino for its horn.

As the camp workers began to pack up around us, Bill leant forward.

"What they leave of the rhino isn't pretty," he said to me, as he pulled his travel-beaten hat down over his tousled brown hair.

We set off in four-wheel drive pick-ups. There is nothing quite like the anticipation of starting an expedition: spirits were high as we kangarooed our way over the uneven ground.

The rest of the day was spent criss-crossing the plains, photographing gazelles, baboons and other creatures we met along the way. We set up camp as dusk began to fall.

Diary continues over the page

TUESDAY 17 JUNE 2008

We awoke to another clear blue sky.

"Today, we'll hopefully be tracking a herd of rhinos," explained our guide, Zollahase. "I'd been told there's a herd in this area, and this morning I found fresh droppings and footprints." Zollahase has been working with rhinos for years and knows very well the threat they face at the hands of poachers. "We have also heard," Zollahase went on, "that poachers are working in this area. I only hope we aren't too late."

As we made our way across the wide open plains, my heart was pounding.

And then the truck ahead of us stopped abruptly.

As the dust cleared, I feared I was about to see for myself exactly what Bill had warned me about the day before. I was right.

It was the saddest thing I had ever seen in my life. Everything about the rhino was perfect, apart from the wounds on its face where its horns used to be. The poachers had left this magnificent beast to rot in the dust. Its life had been dignified but its death had not.

"I did warn you," said Bill, sympathetically. He could see I was shaking with anger and shame at what humans can do.

The leading truck started its engines and hurtled off, like a zebra fleeing a lioness. A crackling voice on the walkie-talkie told us why. It was Zollahase: "I see them, a small herd of 6 or 7 rhinos straight ahead. We will begin to arm!"

A gun, just like the one used by the poachers, was about to bring down another rhino. But we were using tranquilliser darts, not bullets. Through the clinging yellow dust clouds, I could see the herd, running frantically from the trucks. To them we were death. The creatures in these metal beasts stole their brothers and sisters and did not care for the wild at all, so the rhinos ran and ran for cover in the bushes.

It was a magnificent sight. Not that their strides were fuelled by fear but that they were free in the land of their birth. As I watched, Zollahase raised the gun and fired a dart straight into the hide of the largest female. She kept on running, but she gradually slowed and stumbled. Her family were far away when she finally gave in to the tranquilliser. To them she was dead now, but they could not spend time missing her, because they had to think about their own survival.

The rest of the day was spent nursing the sleeping rhino. We winched her into the back of a specially built, reinforced truck and started the journey back to base camp. She was so beautiful we named her Marilyn — after Marilyn Monroe. She weighed almost three quarters of a tonne and her hide was rough and thick, like a dulled suit of armour. Her horns stand proudly on her snout — and that's where they're going to stay.

WEDNESDAY 18 JUNE 2008

Marilyn woke up in a rage on the journey back yesterday, stamping and kicking at the sides of the truck, but by the time we stopped for the night she was relatively quiet. Gordon Caine, the expedition vet, was checking up on her all through the night. When the rest of us got up this morning, she didn't seem to be distressed at all.

Over breakfast I asked Bill what would happen to Marilyn at the Kenyan wildlife reserve. He told me that she would be part of a breeding programme to boost the numbers of black rhino. Eventually, young rhinos would be returned to Namibia.

If Marilyn looked calm during breakfast, her mood certainly changed when it was time to return her to her truck. She was bucking and snorting, as Gordon and his assistants tried to restrain her. After half an hour of tussling, Gordon decided Marilyn would have to be tranquilised one last time.

My adventure has saddened and enlightened me about human beings. People like poachers who kill for profit are capable of such cruelty, but then people like Bill, Gordon and Zollahase are so brave in their fight against the same cruelty.

We were back at base camp by late afternoon. We were greeted by vets from the Kenyan wildlife reserve, eager to check Marilyn over for themselves. Gordon will be travelling to Kenya with Marilyn. Once she's arrived and had a few weeks to get over the journey, she'll be introduced to other rhinos on the reserve. Eventually, Bill hopes that Marilyn will have offspring of her own, playing her part in the recovery of the species.

As I sit watching Marilyn in her reinforced pen, totally oblivious to the journey she's about to make, it all seems like a very long way in the future. But at least her future is secure and now I've seen the dedication of Bill's team I'm sure the future of the black rhino is secure too.

EPILOGUE

FRIDAY 16 NOVEMBER 2012

Totally out of the blue, I got a phone call today from Bill. He said Marilyn was doing fine and that she had settled down in Kenya well. He also told me that she is now a proud mother of two and firmly in charge of the other new rhinos at the reserve.

"She's a kind of mother to them all," said Bill, laughing, and I felt prouder than ever.

Walking With Hunters — Diary

Non-fiction comes in all shapes and sizes. This lovely bit is a diary.
It describes real events and was written day by day on
the author's journey across the plains of Namibia, in Southern Africa.

What to do —

1) Open out the folding pages and read *Walking With Hunters*.
2) When you've read it, think about football for 15 seconds (even if you hate it), then read the whole thing again.
3) Once you've done that, you can go on to the questions.

Turn the page

Inference Questions

6. What impression does the writer give you of what the rhinos' life is like?

1 mark

....

7. **'My adventure has saddened and enlightened me about human beings.'**

Explain Anne's emotions using examples from the text to back up your answer.

2 marks

....

....

....

8. **'As I sit watching Marilyn in her reinforced pen, totally oblivious to the journey she's about to make, it all seems like a very long way in the future.'**

What journey do you think the writer is talking about?

2 marks

....

....

9. **'"She's a kind of mother to them all," said Bill, laughing, and I felt prouder than ever.'**

Why do you think Anne le Trimel was feeling proud?

2 marks

....

....

10. What ideas are we given about poaching from this article?

1 mark

....

Reading Raptors can do inference questions faster than you can eat a chocolate button. How did you do?

Language Questions

For LANGUAGE questions you need to think about why the writer chose to use particular words or phrases — there will be a reason. Read the diary again and try these questions.

1. Find and copy the phrase from Tuesday 17 June that tells you the writer is excited.

.... **1 mark**

2. **'As day broke, I was struck by the sense of calm in the new-born light.'**

Why do you think the writer uses the word **'new-born'**?

.... **2 marks**

....

3. Why do you think the writer uses the word **'kangarooed'** to describe the journey?

.... **1 mark**

4. **'And then the truck ahead of us stopped abruptly.'**

Why do you think the writer wrote this as a sentence all by itself?

.... **1 mark**

5. **'The leading truck started its engines and hurtled off, like a zebra fleeing a lioness.'**

What does this tell you about the way the truck moved?

.... **2 marks**

....

6. **'her hide was rough and thick, like a dulled suit of armour.'**

What is the effect of this simile?

.... **2 marks**

....

AF5

Language Questions

7. Do you think **'Walking With Hunters'** is a good title for the diary?

Explain your answer as fully as you can.

2 marks

....

....

8. 'Through the clinging yellow dust clouds, I could see the herd, running frantically from the trucks.'

a) Underline the two adjectives in the sentence.

1 mark

b) Explain what the writer means by **'clinging yellow dust clouds'**.

....

2 marks

....

9. Why do you think the dead rhino was described as a **'magnificent beast'**?

2 marks

....

....

10. 'He could see I was shaking with anger and shame at what humans can do.'

What does the word '**shaking**' tell you about how Anne le Trimel was feeling?

2 marks

....

....

....

Reading Raptors love language questions more than they love chasing chickens. How did you get on?

Fact Retrieval Questions

FACT RETRIEVAL questions aren't too bad. You just need to pick out facts from the text. Read the diary entries again and see if you can pick out the answers to these questions.

1. The rhino is named

Michaela	**Marjorie**	**Marilyn**	**Marion**

Circle your answer.

1 mark

2. The rhino became more angry as the morning of Wednesday 18 June wore on. Find and copy two words that describe what she was doing to show her anger.

....

....

2 marks

3. The black rhino was going to Kenya

to make new friends	**to be an extra in a wildlife film**	**to be part of a breeding programme**	**to entertain the public**

Put a ring around your choice.

1 mark

4. What is the main purpose of Anne le Trimel's visit?

To take photos of trucks.	**To help save a black rhino from poachers.**	**To meet some interesting characters.**	**To take photos of poachers being caught.**

Put a ring around your choice.

1 mark

5. Write down two ways that guns affect the lives of the rhinos in this piece of writing.

1. ....

2. ....

2 marks

Fact finding is a favourite pastime of Reading Raptors. Tick to show how you got on with these questions.

The last few questions on Walking With Hunters are hidden under there

The Middle Ages to the 1800s

1200s

King John I built up a large collection of animals at the Tower of London. This began a tradition of keeping animals at the Tower that lasted for over six hundred years. European kings sent animals for the collection, including a polar bear and an elephant.

1600s

King James I tried to improve living standards for animals living at the Tower.

1700s

Paying guests were invited into the Tower to see the exhibits for the very first time.

1800s

Scientists finally began to use zoos as centres of study. In 1828 the Zoological Society of London opened the London Zoological Gardens. As people learnt more about the animals kept in zoos, standards started to improve.

Zoos in the Modern World

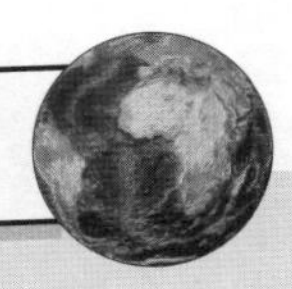

1900s

Once it was commonly known that barred cages cause animals tremendous distress, zoo designs began to change around the world. Open pens with moats were built and the first safari parks were trialled across Europe. These open-style zoos developed captive breeding as a way of saving many of the world's rarest and most unusual creatures from extinction.

Today...

Zoos, wildlife parks and aquariums are extremely popular and serve to educate as well as entertain. In the past, zoos and menageries were only for the rich and powerful: now they are a popular way of teaching everyone about the world we share and how we can give help to the animals who need it most.

Since the present century began, over 150 endangered species have been bred successfully in captivity, helping to ensure the survival of some of the world's rarest creatures.

Glossary

legislation	laws
prosecuted	taken to court
hieroglyphics	Ancient Egyptian picture writing

Turn the page

Born Free? — Non-Fiction

Non-fiction texts are any bits of writing that tell you facts, or are about something that really happened. A science book is non-fiction, and so is a newspaper or magazine. Read the text, read it again, and then go on to the questions.

Born Free?

For over 2500 years, humans have been keeping wild and exotic animals. Some kept these animals to show off their wealth and power, others kept them for entertainment and pleasure. More recently, animals have been kept for scientific study and conservation.

Amazingly, it was not until the twentieth century that people began to think about the special requirements of wild and exotic animals in captivity. Many animals died of starvation and cruelty before new legislation was passed in the early 1990s, which said that anyone who did not give captive wild animals proper care could be prosecuted.

Below, Ellen Merinat of the RSPCA charts the development of the zoo from its earliest beginnings up to the present day, with some startling findings!

2500 BC

In Ancient Egyptian tombs, hieroglyphics show that wealthy Egyptians kept many wild and unusual species from their local environment, including monkeys, birds and big cats such as cheetahs.

1500 BC

Further records show that Egyptian Queen Hatshepsut sent an expedition to the Red Sea to capture leopards for her private collection.

500 BC

Old paintings and carvings show that the Ancient Greeks had collections of exotic birds — it is thought that these were the first collections open to the public, and visitors were charged a small entry fee.

200 BC

Written evidence from the time of the Romans tells us that the rich enjoyed keeping private collections of animals, just to show off their wealth. The Romans also used wild animals as part of the entertainment at gladiator fights.

Writer's Purpose Questions

Think about how reading the text makes you feel — it'll help with these WRITER'S PURPOSE questions.

1. How does the writer make you feel when she writes about finding the dead rhino?

2 marks

....

....

2. Anne's diary begins with a description of the **'sense of calm'** she felt. Why do you think she started by describing this? Refer to the text in your answer.

3 marks

....

....

....

3. The writer refers to the journey in the trucks throughout the diary. Why do you think she does this? Refer to the text in your answer.

3 marks

....

....

....

4. What does the writer think about poaching? How can you tell? Refer to the text in your answer.

3 marks

....

....

....

....

Reading Raptors are great at working out what the writer is trying to make the reader feel. Can you?

AF4 Structure and Layout Questions

In STRUCTURE and LAYOUT questions you need to think about why a piece of writing has boxes, subheadings or other fancy features. See if you can answer these questions.

1. Why is the information in the shaded boxes broken up into three sections?

....

....

2 marks

2. Why do you think the information about Ellen Merinat has been put into a separate box?

....

1 mark

3. How do the titles on the shaded boxes help you to understand the writing?

....

1 mark

4. What is the purpose of the glossary?

....

....

2 marks

5. Number the boxes to show the order these events took place.

One has been done for you.

☐	**Ancient Greeks collected birds**
1	**Hieroglyphics show early animal collections**
☐	**Paying guests can visit the animals in the Tower of London**
☐	**A polar bear and an elephant sent to the Tower of London**

2 marks

Reading Raptors can do layout questions blindfolded.
How did you get on with these questions?

Writer's Purpose Questions

Writers have a reason for writing what they write — that's a bit of a tongue twister, but it's true, and that's what these WRITER'S PURPOSE questions are all about. Read the article again and have a go at these questions.

1. What is the purpose of the writing in the shaded boxes?

....

1 mark

2. The first paragraph

identifies the key words in the text	introduces the main points of the text	asks whether zoos are cruel	tells you about the author

1 mark

Put a ring around your choice.

3. a) Who do you think this text is written for?

Kings and queens	Poachers	Animal lovers	Teachers

1 mark

Circle your answer.

b) Explain your answer to part **a)** with reference to the text.

....

....

2 marks

4. **'Scientists finally began to use zoos as centres of study.'**
Why do you think that Ellen uses the word '**finally**' in this sentence?

....

....

1 mark

Reading Raptors know what the writer's goal is as soon as they've read the text. How about you?

Fact Retrieval Questions

FACT RETRIEVAL questions ask for some information or a word that can be found in the text. Have another read of the article and see if you can find the answers to these questions.

1. In the first sentence, the writer tells us that humans have been keeping animals

as pets and working animals	**for hundreds of years**	**in cages and pens**	**for over 2500 years**

1 mark

Circle your choice.

2. When did zoos first become important to scientific study?

2000 BC	**1200s**	**500 BC**	**1800s**

1 mark

Circle your choice.

3. Which civilisation of people first introduced the concept of paying to see animals?

....

1 mark

4. When were laws introduced about the mistreatment of animals?

....

1 mark

5. The information in the text tells us

the history of the RSPCA	**the history of animal collections and zoos**	**the history of archaeology**	**the history of cruelty to animals**

1 mark

Put a ring around your choice.

Fact Retrieval Questions

6. Write down one way we know about animal collections in the ancient world.

....

1 mark

7. Since the 1900s, conditions for animals have

seen many more animals die from neglect	shown a decline in the popularity of zoos	improved due to new ideas and laws	put more people behind bars

1 mark

Put a ring around your choice.

8. Use information from **'Born Free?'** to complete this chart.

1500 BC	**Queen Hatshepsut sends an expedition to capture leopards**
	Animal collection started at the Tower of London by King John I
1700s	
	The Zoological Society of London opens the London Zoological Gardens
Today...	**Zoos and wildlife parks are going from strength to strength through captive breeding programmes**

3 marks

9. Draw lines to match the different periods of history with the statements.
One has been done for you.

The Romans	**had large public collections of wild birds**
In the Middle Ages they	**captured wild animals to fight humans**
The Greeks	**keep animals to protect them from extinction**
Zoos today	**kept animals in the Tower of London**

2 marks

Reading Raptors are always on a fact finding quest.
Are you? Tick to show how these questions went.

AF3

Inference Questions

INFERENCE questions can ask you things like how you think a character feels, or what exactly is happening, even if the text doesn't say it directly. Use your reading skills to have a go at these questions...

1. What do you think the author means when she says **'with some startling findings'**? Refer to the text in your answer.

2 marks

....

....

2. Many different animals were sent to the Tower of London zoo. Why do you think Ellen Merinat chose to mention the polar bear and the elephant?

1 mark

....

3. How do you know that attitudes to keeping wild animals have changed?

2 marks

....

....

4. Which do you think is the most likely reason that the Zoological Society of London opened the London Zoological Gardens in 1828?

To train animals for circuses	**To discover more about animals**	**To make lots of money to fund expeditions**	**To show off how rich the society was**

1 mark

Circle your choice.

5. Do you think that King James I cared about animals? Explain your answer.

1 mark

....

The last few questions on Born Free? are under here

Roll Up! Roll Up! — Newspaper Article

Newspapers usually try to give a balanced view, and talk about how different people feel about the same thing. Read and re-read this article, then have a stab at the questions.

Roll Up! Roll Up!

Animal rights groups in uproar as European circus comes to town

Animal rights campaigners are threatening to demonstrate outside Roddy Baker's European Circus if it is allowed to open its doors to the public in two weeks' time.

Anthony Brown, the national director of Fair Play For Animals, told us in an in-depth interview, that the circus was well-known for keeping animals such as tigers, elephants, bears and lions in cramped cages as they tour around the world.

He said: "It's as if everyone is turning a blind eye to the cruelty because these animals perform tricks. They are starved and beaten to make them perform but no-one seems to mind. By letting them perform in this country we are saying that we approve of this kind of torture."

Mr Brown, who was speaking from his London headquarters, threatened a long and sustained protest against the circus, which he went on to describe as "horrific and barbaric".

The circus has been in operation for over fifty years and was started by Jan-Eric Rubensson, a Scandinavian mink farmer, who later changed his name to Roddy Baker.

His son, the circus's current owner Roddy Baker Jnr, told me, "In the fifties, people hadn't seen wild and exotic creatures like tigers and elephants up close before, so my dad's circus became a huge success. I've taken it further and further and introduced new animals, such as our brown bears and our crocodile. People don't see these things every day, so they will always pay good money to do just that.

"I can hardly move for international regulations about keeping animals and I have to abide by them or I get shut down and put out of business. What would happen to the animals then? I couldn't return them to the wild — they would never survive and I couldn't afford to keep them myself, so I would have to sell them, and goodness knows what would happen to them then."

When asked about the accusations of beating and starving, Mr Baker Jnr retorted, "Damned if I do and damned if I don't. If the inspectors caught me beating my animals I'd be in big trouble. All my animals are perfectly healthy. They enjoy doing the tricks and people are happy to pay to see them."

Roddy Baker Jnr: "all my animals are perfectly healthy."

Government ministers failed to comment on the demonstrations, saying only that European relations have been strained recently and that further conclusive evidence would have to be found before any action would be taken against Mr Baker and his circus.

The circus opens on Tuesday 18 June in London's West End. Tickets are already selling fast, but as Mr Brown pointed out, "We've got video tape proving these animals are suffering — once people see it on TV, sales will dry up and he'll have to move on."

A full review will appear in Saturday's edition.

Turn the page

Inference Questions

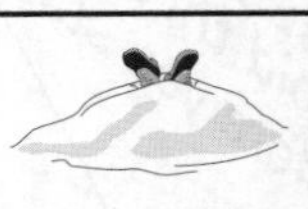

6. **'Written evidence from the time of the Romans tells us that the rich enjoyed keeping private collections of animals, just to show off their wealth.'**
   What does the way this sentence is written tell us about Ellen Merinat's feelings towards the rich Romans?

   ....

   ....

   2 marks

Context Questions

CONTEXT questions are about relating the text to the wider world. Have a final read through of the text and see if you can answer these questions.

1. Why do you think there is far more information from the 1900s and today than from the other centuries?

   ....

   ....

   1 mark

2. **'Born Free?'** is a non-fiction text.
   Tick two boxes to show the features of non-fiction texts.

Written in the present tense	☐
Contains facts	☐
Contains a timeline	☐
Based on reality	☐
Gives the author's life story	☐
Contains made-up characters	☐

   2 marks

Reading Raptors can do these questions faster than you can say 'Raptors rule'. How did you get on?

Unfold these pages before you start

AF2 Fact Retrieval Questions

For FACT RETRIEVAL questions you need to think like a fact finding detective. Carefully read through the article and see if you can pick out the answers to these questions.

1. What is the name of the organisation Anthony Brown works for?

....

1 mark

2. What two ways of stopping the circus does Anthony Brown threaten to use?

....

....

2 marks

3. Give two ways in which Anthony Brown claims the animals are mistreated.

....

....

2 marks

4. How has Roddy Baker Jnr changed the circus since he took it over from his father?

....

1 mark

5. What does Roddy Baker Jnr say he would have to do with the animals in his care if the circus was forced to close down?

....

1 mark

6. How does Roddy Baker Jnr explain that he couldn't be cruel to his animals?

....

....

1 mark

AF2

Fact Retrieval Questions

7. What was the real name of Roddy Baker Jnr's father?

....

1 mark

8. Anthony Brown thinks that Roddy Baker Jnr is

cruel to animals	**a zoo keeper**	**concerned about animals**	**stupid**

Circle your answer.

1 mark

9. Why does Roddy Baker Jnr think that his circus is so popular?

....

....

2 marks

10. Which of the following facts can be found in this text? Tick **two** boxes.

The circus opens on Tuesday 18 June ☐

The government supports Roddy Baker Jnr ☐

Animal rights campaigners want to try to steal the animals from the circus ☐

The circus has been in operation for over fifty years ☐

Not many tickets have been sold for the first performance ☐

2 marks

11. What does Anthony Brown say that people will think if the circus is allowed to perform in Britain?

....

1 mark

Reading Raptors can find facts faster than you can jump in the air and shout 'T-rex!' How about you?

Inference Questions

INFERENCE questions are all about understanding what you've read. You have to find clues in the writing to work out what's really going on. See if you can work out the answers to these.

1. Anthony Brown sounds

stupid and over-confident	**angry and concerned**	**bitter and sarcastic**	**happy and lighthearted**

Circle your answer and explain it on the lines below with reference to the text.

2 marks

....

....

2. 'Damned if I do and damned if I don't.'

What does this statement tell you about Roddy Baker Jnr's character?

1 mark

....

3. 'We've got video tape proving these animals are suffering — once people see it on TV, sales will dry up and he'll have to move on.'

How would you describe this statement? Circle your answer.

A threat	**Blackmail**	**A fact**	**A compliment**

1 mark

4. 'European relations have been strained recently and that further conclusive evidence would have to be found before any action would be taken'

Do you think that the government wants the circus to go ahead?

Explain your answer as fully as you can.

2 marks

....

....

Reading Raptors can do inference questions whilst jumping like a jelly bean. How did you do?

Structure and Layout Questions

Writers think very carefully about how they STRUCTURE their writing and the LAYOUT of it on the page. Read through the article and think about why it has been presented like it is.

1. Label each arrow to identify the different parts of the article.

Headline **Subheading**

Caption **Summary of article**

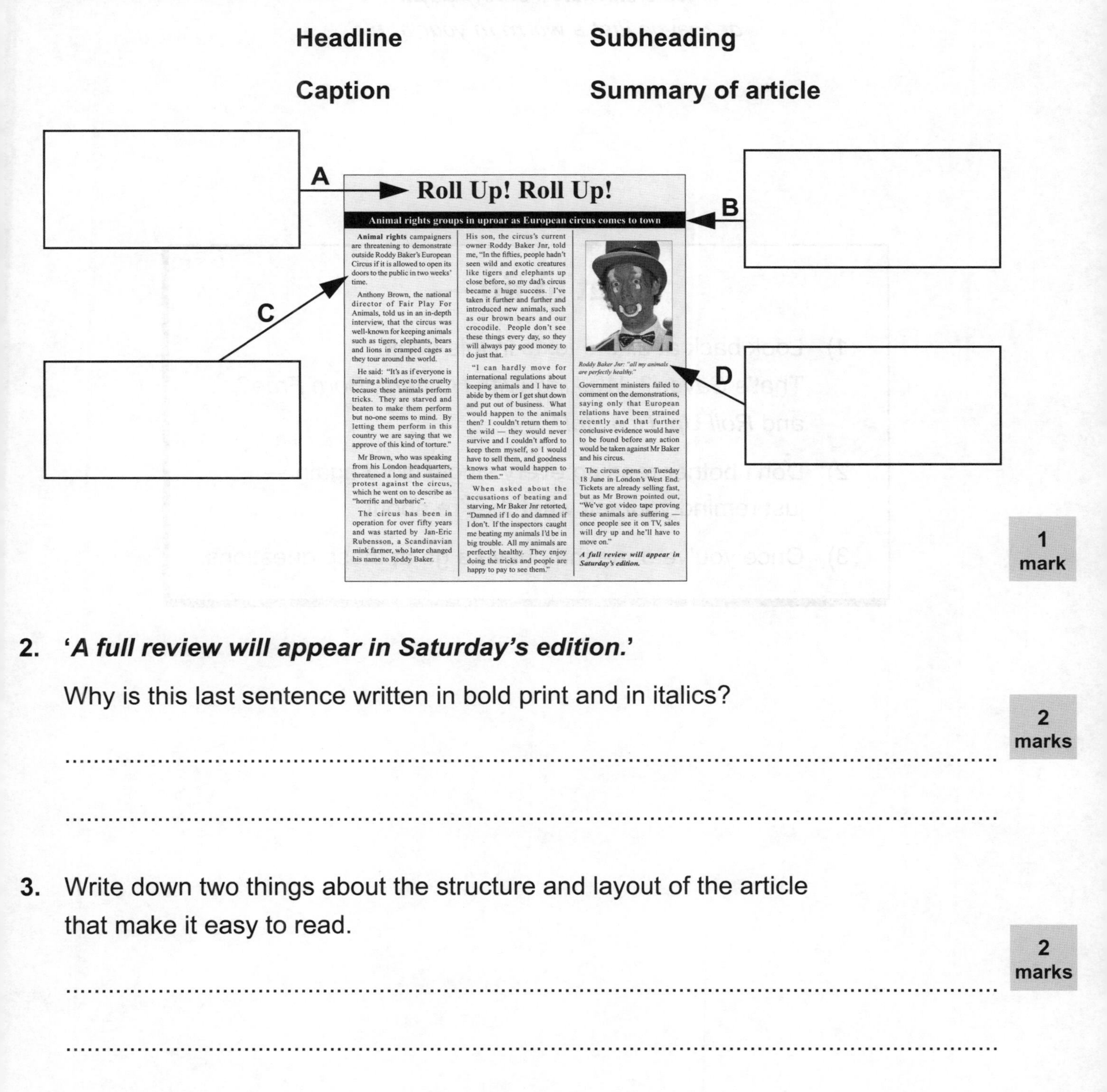

Roll Up! Roll Up!

Animal rights groups in uproar as European circus comes to town

Animal rights campaigners are threatening to demonstrate outside Roddy Baker's European Circus if it is allowed to open its doors to the public in two weeks' time.

Anthony Brown, the national director of Fair Play For Animals, told us in an in-depth interview, that the circus was well-known for keeping animals such as tigers, elephants, bears and lions in cramped cages as they tour around the world.

He said: "It's as if everyone is turning a blind eye to the cruelty because these animals perform tricks. They are starved and beaten to make them perform but no-one seems to mind. By letting them perform in this country we are saying that we approve of this kind of torture."

Mr Brown, who was speaking from his London headquarters, threatened a long and sustained protest against the circus, which he went on to describe as "horrific and barbaric".

The circus has been in operation for over fifty years and was started by Jan-Eric Rubensson, a Scandinavian mink farmer, who later changed his name to Roddy Baker.

His son, the circus's current owner Roddy Baker Jnr, told me, "In the fifties, people hadn't seen wild and exotic creatures like tigers and elephants up close before, so my dad's circus became a huge success. I've taken it further and further and introduced new animals, such as our brown bears and our crocodile. People don't see these things every day, so they will always pay good money to do just that.

"I can hardly move for international regulations about keeping animals and I have to abide by them or I get shut down and put out of business. What would happen to the animals then? I couldn't return them to the wild — they would never survive and I couldn't afford to keep them myself, so I would have to sell them, and goodness knows what would happen to them then."

When asked about the accusations of beating and starving, Mr Baker Jnr retorted, "Damned if I do and damned if I don't. If the inspectors caught me beating my animals I'd be in big trouble. All my animals are perfectly healthy. They enjoy doing the tricks and people are happy to pay to see them."

Roddy Baker Jnr: "all my animals are perfectly healthy."

Government ministers failed to comment on the demonstrations, saying only that European relations have been strained recently and that further conclusive evidence would have to be found before any action would be taken against Mr Baker and his circus.

The circus opens on Tuesday 18 June in London's West End. Tickets are already selling fast, but as Mr Brown pointed out, "We've got video tape proving these animals are suffering — once people see it on TV, sales will dry up and he'll have to move on."

A full review will appear in Saturday's edition.

1 mark

2. ***'A full review will appear in Saturday's edition.'***

Why is this last sentence written in bold print and in italics?

2 marks

....

....

3. Write down two things about the structure and layout of the article that make it easy to read.

2 marks

....

....

Reading Raptors can do layout questions faster than wizards can wave their wands. How about you?

Questions On The Whole Lot

At the end of the test you always get a few questions covering all the texts...
like the cherry on your bun...
grated cheese on your spaghetti...
ice cream on a sunny day...
or maybe just a worm in your apple.

What to do —

1) Look back at all the texts in this book. That's *Saved?*, *Walking With Hunters, Born Free?* and *Roll Up! Roll Up!*
2) Don't bother reading every single word again — just remind yourself what they're about.
3) Once you've done that, have a go at these questions.

The questions start over there ➡

Questions On The Whole Lot

You'll need to think back to all of the texts that you've read in this book when you're answering these questions. Ready... set... go...

1. In which text would you expect to find factual information about animal collections?

Walking With Hunters	Roll Up! Roll Up!	Saved?	Born Free?

Circle your answer.

1 mark

2. Which piece of writing was written by a journalist?

Walking With Hunters	Roll Up! Roll Up!	Saved?	Born Free?

Circle your answer.

1 mark

3. Where would you find information about poaching?

Walking With Hunters	Roll Up! Roll Up!	Saved?	Born Free?

Circle your answer.

1 mark

4. Match up the names of the texts to the description of what each text is about.

One has been done for you.

Roll Up! Roll Up!	**Facts about the history of zoos**
Saved? ———	**Poem from an animal's point of view**
Born Free?	**Account of an expedition to catch a rhino**
Walking With Hunters	**Argument about a circus**

2 marks

Questions On The Whole Lot

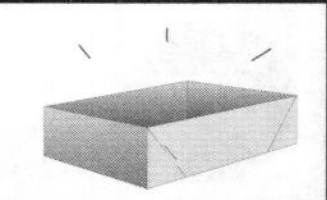

5. The texts give **information** about animals in captivity.
Which **three** of the following can also be found in the texts? Tick three boxes **only**.

Entertainment ☐

Directions ☐

Instructions ☐

Balanced argument ☐

Opinion ☐

2 marks

6. These sentences have been left out of the texts you have read.
Draw lines to match each sentence to the text you think it came from.

A rhino was lying dead on the ground.	**Roll Up! Roll Up!**
Many Chinese emperors had large collections of animals.	**Saved?**
The demonstrators will camp outside and stop people from getting in.	**Born Free?**
My brothers were nowhere to be found.	**Walking With Hunters**

2 marks

7. Put ticks to show which statements about man's treatment of animals are true and which statements are false.

	true	false
In the late 1990s, a zoo keeper who didn't give his animals enough food couldn't be prosecuted.		
Poachers kill rhinos just for their skins — their horns aren't very valuable.		
Zoos are only for people's entertainment.		
People who are proved to have mistreated animals are punished.		
A lion probably wouldn't notice if it was taken from its natural habitat and put in a cage in a zoo.		

2 marks

E6R322